STRANGER THINGS

WWW.DANILO.COM

Published by Danilo Promotions Ltd. Unit 3, The io Centre, Lea Road, Waltham Abbey, EN9 1AS, England.
Enquiries: **info@danilo.com** For all other information: **www.danilo.com**
Manufactured in China.

While every effort is made to ensure that the information included in this diary is correct, Danilo Promotions Ltd. cannot be held
responsible for errors and omissions. The Banking and Financial Dealings Act, 1971, allows the Government to alter dates at short notice.
Danilo is committed to making all of its products fully recyclable.

PERSONAL INFORMATION

NAME:

ADDRESS:

MOBILE:

EMAIL:

IN CASE OF EMERGENCY PLEASE CONTACT

NAME:

ADDRESS:

MOBILE:

DOCTOR:

DOCTOR TELEPHONE:

KNOWN ALLERGIES:

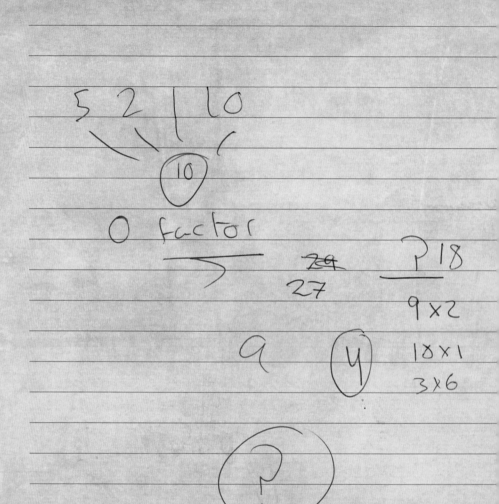

NOTES

5 2 | 10

(10)

0 factor

27 / ~~29~~ P 18 / 9 × 2

9   (4)   18 × 1
          3 × 6

(?)

DUSTIN

JANUARY

WK	M	T	W	T	F	S	S
52						1	2
1	3	4	5	6	7	8	9
2	10	11	12	13	14	15	16
3	17	18	19	20	21	22	23
4	24	25	26	27	28	29	30
5	31						

FEBRUARY

WK	M	T	W	T	F	S	S
5		1	2	3	4	5	6
6	7	8	9	10	11	12	13
7	14	15	16	17	18	19	20
8	21	22	23	24	25	26	27
9	28						

MARCH

WK	M	T	W	T	F	S	S
9		1	2	3	4	5	6
10	7	8	9	10	11	12	13
11	14	15	16	17	18	19	20
12	21	22	23	24	25	26	27
13	28	29	30	31			

APRIL

WK	M	T	W	T	F	S	S
13					1	2	3
14	4	5	6	7	8	9	10
15	11	12	13	14	15	16	17
16	18	19	20	21	22	23	24
17	25	26	27	28	29	30	

MAY

WK	M	T	W	T	F	S	S
17							1
18	2	3	4	5	6	7	8
19	9	10	11	12	13	14	15
20	16	17	18	19	20	21	22
21	23	24	25	26	27	28	29
22	30	31					

JUNE

WK	M	T	W	T	F	S	S
22			1	2	3	4	5
23	6	7	8	9	10	11	12
24	13	14	15	16	17	18	19
25	20	21	22	23	24	25	26
26	27	28	29	30			

JULY

WK	M	T	W	T	F	S	S
26					1	2	3
27	4	5	6	7	8	9	10
28	11	12	13	14	15	16	17
29	18	19	20	21	22	23	24
30	25	26	27	28	29	30	31

AUGUST

WK	M	T	W	T	F	S	S
31	1	2	3	4	5	6	7
32	8	9	10	11	12	13	14
33	15	16	17	18	19	20	21
34	22	23	24	25	26	27	28
35	29	30	31				

SEPTEMBER

WK	M	T	W	T	F	S	S
35				1	2	3	4
36	5	6	7	8	9	10	11
37	12	13	14	15	16	17	18
38	19	20	21	22	23	24	25
39	26	27	28	29	30		

OCTOBER

WK	M	T	W	T	F	S	S
39						1	2
40	3	4	5	6	7	8	9
41	10	11	12	13	14	15	16
42	17	18	19	20	21	22	23
43	24	25	26	27	28	29	30
44	31						

NOVEMBER

WK	M	T	W	T	F	S	S
44		1	2	3	4	5	6
45	7	8	9	10	11	12	13
46	14	15	16	17	18	19	20
47	21	22	23	24	25	26	27
48	28	29	30				

DECEMBER

WK	M	T	W	T	F	S	S
48				1	2	3	4
49	5	6	7	8	9	10	11
50	12	13	14	15	16	17	18
51	19	20	21	22	23	24	25
52	26	27	28	29	30	31	

JANUARY

WK	M	T	W	T	F	S	S
52							1
1	2	3	4	5	6	7	8
2	9	10	11	12	13	14	15
3	16	17	18	19	20	21	22
4	23	24	25	26	27	28	29
5	30	31					

FEBRUARY

WK	M	T	W	T	F	S	S
5			1	2	3	4	5
6	6	7	8	9	10	11	12
7	13	14	15	16	17	18	19
8	20	21	22	23	24	25	26
9	27	28					

MARCH

WK	M	T	W	T	F	S	S
9			1	2	3	4	5
10	6	7	8	9	10	11	12
11	13	14	15	16	17	18	19
12	20	21	22	23	24	25	26
13	27	28	29	30	31		

APRIL

WK	M	T	W	T	F	S	S
13						1	2
14	3	4	5	6	7	8	9
15	10	11	12	13	14	15	16
16	17	18	19	20	21	22	23
17	24	25	26	27	28	29	30

MAY

WK	M	T	W	T	F	S	S
18	1	2	3	4	5	6	7
19	8	9	10	11	12	13	14
20	15	16	17	18	19	20	21
21	22	23	24	25	26	27	28
22	29	30	31				

JUNE

WK	M	T	W	T	F	S	S
22				1	2	3	4
23	5	6	7	8	9	10	11
24	12	13	14	15	16	17	18
25	19	20	21	22	23	24	25
26	26	27	28	29	30		

JULY

WK	M	T	W	T	F	S	S
26						1	2
27	3	4	5	6	7	8	9
28	10	11	12	13	14	15	16
29	17	18	19	20	21	22	23
30	24	25	26	27	28	29	30
31	31						

AUGUST

WK	M	T	W	T	F	S	S
31		1	2	3	4	5	6
32	7	8	9	10	11	12	13
33	14	15	16	17	18	19	20
34	21	22	23	24	25	26	27
35	28	29	30	31			

SEPTEMBER

WK	M	T	W	T	F	S	S
35					1	2	3
36	4	5	6	7	8	9	10
37	11	12	13	14	15	16	17
38	18	19	20	21	22	23	24
39	25	26	27	28	29	30	

OCTOBER

WK	M	T	W	T	F	S	S
39							1
40	2	3	4	5	6	7	8
41	9	10	11	12	13	14	15
42	16	17	18	19	20	21	22
43	23	24	25	26	27	28	29
44	30	31					

NOVEMBER

WK	M	T	W	T	F	S	S
44			1	2	3	4	5
45	6	7	8	9	10	11	12
46	13	14	15	16	17	18	19
47	20	21	22	23	24	25	26
48	27	28	29	30			

DECEMBER

WK	M	T	W	T	F	S	S
48					1	2	3
49	4	5	6	7	8	9	10
50	11	12	13	14	15	16	17
51	18	19	20	21	22	23	24
52	25	26	27	28	29	30	31

2022

NEW YEAR'S DAY	JAN 1
NEW YEAR'S DAY HOLIDAY	JAN 3
BANK HOLIDAY (SCOTLAND)	JAN 4
CHINESE NEW YEAR (TIGER)	FEB 1
VALENTINE'S DAY	FEB 14
ST. DAVID'S DAY (WALES) / SHROVE TUESDAY	MAR 1
ST. PATRICK'S DAY	MAR 17
DAYLIGHT SAVING TIME STARTS / MOTHERING SUNDAY	MAR 27
RAMADAN BEGINS	APR 2
GOOD FRIDAY / PASSOVER BEGINS	APR 15
EASTER SUNDAY	APR 17
EASTER MONDAY	APR 18
ST. GEORGE'S DAY	APR 23
EARLY MAY BANK HOLIDAY	MAY 2
QUEEN'S PLATINUM JUBILEE BANK HOLIDAY	JUN 2
QUEEN'S PLATINUM JUBILEE BANK HOLIDAY	JUN 3
FATHER'S DAY	JUN 19
BATTLE OF THE BOYNE (NORTHERN IRELAND)	JUL 12
ISLAMIC NEW YEAR BEGINS	JUL 29
SUMMER BANK HOLIDAY (SCOTLAND)	AUG 1
SUMMER BANK HOLIDAY (ENG, NIR, WAL)	AUG 29
THE UNITED NATIONS INTERNATIONAL DAY OF PEACE	SEPT 21
ROSH HASHANAH (JEWISH NEW YEAR) BEGINS	SEPT 25
YOM KIPPUR BEGINS	OCT 4
WORLD MENTAL HEALTH DAY	OCT 10
DIWALI	OCT 24
DAYLIGHT SAVING TIME ENDS	OCT 30
HALLOWEEN	OCT 31
GUY FAWKES NIGHT	NOV 5
REMEMBRANCE SUNDAY	NOV 13
ST. ANDREW'S DAY (SCOTLAND)	NOV 30
CHRISTMAS DAY	DEC 25
BOXING DAY	DEC 26
BANK HOLIDAY	DEC 27
NEW YEAR'S EVE	DEC 31

JANUARY	FEBRUARY	MARCH
1 S	1 T	1 T
2 S	2 W	2 W
3 M	3 T	3 T
4 T	4 F	4 F
5 W	5 S	5 S
6 T	6 S	6 S
7 F	7 M	7 M
8 S	8 T	8 T
9 S	9 W	9 W
10 M	10 T	10 T
11 T	11 F	11 F
12 W	12 S	12 S
13 T	13 S	13 S
14 F	14 M	14 M
15 S	15 T	15 T
16 S	16 W	16 W
17 M	17 T	17 T
18 T	18 F	18 F
19 W	19 S	19 S
20 T	20 S	20 S
21 F	21 M	21 M
22 S	22 T	22 T
23 S	23 W	23 W
24 M	24 T	24 T
25 T	25 F	25 F
26 W	26 S	26 S
27 T	27 S	27 S
28 F	28 M	28 M
29 S		29 T
30 S		30 W
31 M		31 T

APRIL	MAY	JUNE
1 F	1 S	1 W
2 S	2 M	2 T
3 S	3 T	3 F
4 M	4 W	4 S
5 T	5 T	5 S
6 W	6 F	6 M
7 T	7 S	7 T
8 F	8 S	8 W
9 S	9 M	9 T
10 S	10 T	10 F
11 M	11 W	11 S
12 T	12 T	12 S
13 W	13 F	13 M
14 T	14 S	14 T
15 F	15 S	15 W
16 S	16 M	16 T
17 S	17 T	17 F
18 M	18 W	18 S
19 T	19 T	19 S
20 W	20 F	20 M
21 T	21 S	21 T
22 F	22 S	22 W
23 S	23 M	23 T
24 S	24 T	24 F
25 M	25 W	25 S
26 T	26 T	26 S
27 W	27 F	27 M
28 T	28 S	28 T
29 F	29 S	29 W
30 S	30 M	30 T
	31 T	

PLANNER 2022

JULY	AUGUST	SEPTEMBER
1 F	1 M	1 T
2 S	2 T	2 F
3 S	3 W	3 S
4 M	4 T	4 S
5 T	5 F	5 M
6 W	6 S	6 T
7 T	7 S	7 W
8 F	8 M	8 T
9 S	9 T	9 F
10 S	10 W	10 S
11 M	11 T	11 S
12 T	12 F	12 M
13 W	13 S	13 T
14 T	14 S	14 W
15 F	15 M	15 T
16 S	16 T	16 F
17 S	17 W	17 S
18 M	18 T	18 S
19 T	19 F	19 M
20 W	20 S	20 T
21 T	21 S	21 W
22 F	22 M	22 T
23 S	23 T	23 F
24 S	24 W	24 S
25 M	25 T	25 S
26 T	26 F	26 M
27 W	27 S	27 T
28 T	28 S	28 W
29 F	29 M	29 T
30 S	30 T	30 F
31 S	31 W	

OCTOBER

1	S
2	S
3	M
4	T
5	W
6	T
7	F
8	S
9	S
10	M
11	T
12	W
13	T
14	F
15	S
16	S
17	M
18	T
19	W
20	T
21	F
22	S
23	S
24	M
25	T
26	W
27	T
28	F
29	S
30	S
31	M

NOVEMBER

1	T
2	W
3	T
4	F
5	S
6	S
7	M
8	T
9	W
10	T
11	F
12	S
13	S
14	M
15	T
16	W
17	T
18	F
19	S
20	S
21	M
22	T
23	W
24	T
25	F
26	S
27	S
28	M
29	T
30	W

DECEMBER

1	T
2	F
3	S
4	S
5	M
6	T
7	W
8	T
9	F
10	S
11	S
12	M
13	T
14	W
15	T
16	F
17	S
18	S
19	M
20	T
21	W
22	T
23	F
24	S
25	S
26	M
27	T
28	W
29	T
30	F
31	S

COVER COVER
UP UP

hnl

HAWKINS NATIONAL LABORATORY
U.S. DEPT OF ENERGY

THE
UPSIDE
DOWN

DIMENSION

GATE

TO DO

....

....

....

....

....

....

....

....

....

....

....

....

....

....

....

....

DECEMBER 2021

27 MONDAY

28 TUESDAY

29 WEDNESDAY

30 THURSDAY

New Year's Eve

New Year's Day

SATURDAY 1

SUNDAY 2

NOTES

HAM RADIO
HAWKINS, INDIANA

T	F	S	S	M	T	W	T	F	S	S	M	T	W	T	F	S	S	M	T	W	T	F	S	S	M	T	W	T	F	S
16	17	18	19	20	21	22	23	24	25	26	27	28	29	30	31	1	2	3	4	5	6	7	8	9	10	11	12	13	14	15

JANUARY 2022

3 MONDAY

New Year's Day Holiday

4 TUESDAY

Bank Holiday (Scotland)

5 WEDNESDAY

6 THURSDAY

FRIDAY 7

SATURDAY 8

SUNDAY 9

NOTES

10 MONDAY

11 TUESDAY

12 WEDNESDAY

13 THURSDAY

SATURDAY 15

SUNDAY 16

NOTES

JANUARY 2022

17 MONDAY

18 TUESDAY

19 WEDNESDAY

20 THURSDAY

FRIDAY 21

SATURDAY 22

SUNDAY 23

NOTES

S	S	M	T	W	T	F	S	S	M	T	W	T	F	S	S	M	T	W	T	F	S	S	M	T	W	T	F	S	S	M
1	2	3	4	5	6	7	8	9	10	11	12	13	14	15	16	17	18	19	20	21	22	23	24	25	26	27	28	29	30	31

24 MONDAY

25 TUESDAY

26 WEDNESDAY

27 THURSDAY

FRIDAY 28

SATURDAY 29

SUNDAY 30

NOTES

S S M T W T F S S M T W T F S S M T W T F S S M T W T F S S M
1 2 3 4 5 6 7 8 9 10 11 12 13 14 15 16 17 18 19 20 21 22 23 24 25 26 27 28 29 30 31

FEBRUARY

TO DO ....

....

....

....

....

....

....

....

....

....

....

....

....

....

31 MONDAY

1 TUESDAY

Chinese New Year (Tiger)

2 WEDNESDAY

3 THURSDAY

FRIDAY 4

SATURDAY 5

SUNDAY 6

NOTES

S	M	T	W	T	F	S	S	M	T	W	T	F	S	S	M	T	W	T	F	S	S	M	T	W	T	F	S	S	M	T
16	17	18	19	20	21	22	23	24	25	26	27	28	29	30	31	1	2	3	4	5	6	7	8	9	10	11	12	13	14	15

FEBRUARY 2022

7 **MONDAY**

8 **TUESDAY**

9 **WEDNESDAY**

10 **THURSDAY**

F

FRIDAY 11

SATURDAY 12

SUNDAY 13

NOTES

T	W	T	F	S	S	M	T	W	T	F	S	S	M	T	W	T	F	S	S	M	T	W	T	F	S	S	M
1	2	3	4	5	6	7	8	9	10	11	12	13	14	15	16	17	18	19	20	21	22	23	24	25	26	27	28

14 MONDAY

15 TUESDAY

16 WEDNESDAY

17 THURSDAY

FRIDAY 18

F

SATURDAY 19

SUNDAY 20

NOTES

T	W	T	F	S	S	M	T	W	T	F	S	S	M	T	W	T	F	S	S	M	T	W	T	F	S	S	M
1	2	3	4	5	6	7	8	9	10	11	12	13	14	15	16	17	18	19	20	21	22	23	24	25	26	27	28

FEBRUARY 2022

21 MONDAY

22 TUESDAY

23 WEDNESDAY

24 THURSDAY

FRIDAY 25

F

SATURDAY 26

SUNDAY 27

NOTES

T	W	T	F	S	S	M	T	W	T	F	S	S	M	T	W	T	F	S	S	M	T	W	T	F	S	S	M
1	2	3	4	5	6	7	8	9	10	11	12	13	14	15	16	17	18	19	20	21	22	23	24	25	26	27	28

TO DO

28 MONDAY

1 TUESDAY

St. David's Day (Wales) / Shrove Tuesday

2 WEDNESDAY

3 THURSDAY

FRIDAY 4

SATURDAY 5

SUNDAY 6

NOTES

7 MONDAY

8 TUESDAY

9 WEDNESDAY

10 THURSDAY

FRIDAY 11

M

SATURDAY 12

SUNDAY 13

NOTES

CAMP
85
KNOW WHERE

T	W	T	F	S	S	M	T	W	T	F	S	S	M	T	W	T	F	S	S	M	T	W	T	F	S	S	M	T	W	T
1	2	3	4	5	6	7	8	9	10	11	12	13	14	15	16	17	18	19	20	21	22	23	24	25	26	27	28	29	30	31

14 MONDAY

15 TUESDAY

16 WEDNESDAY

17 THURSDAY

St. Patrick's Day

FRIDAY 18

M

SATURDAY 19

SUNDAY 20

NOTES

T	W	T	F	S	S	M	T	W	T	F	S	S	M	T	W	T	F	S	S	M	T	W	T	F	S	S	M	T	W	T
1	2	3	4	5	6	7	8	9	10	11	12	13	14	15	16	17	18	19	20	21	22	23	24	25	26	27	28	29	30	31

21 MONDAY

22 TUESDAY

23 WEDNESDAY

24 THURSDAY

FRIDAY 25

M

SATURDAY 26

Daylight Saving Time Starts / Mothering Sunday

SUNDAY 27

NOTES

T	W	T	F	S	S	M	T	W	T	F	S	S	M	T	W	T	F	S	S	M	T	W	T	F	S	S	M	T	W	T
1	2	3	4	5	6	7	8	9	10	11	12	13	14	15	16	17	18	19	20	21	22	23	24	25	26	27	28	29	30	31

APRIL

TO DO ....
....
....
....
....
....
....
....
....
....
....
....
....
....
....
....

MARCH 2022

28 MONDAY

29 TUESDAY

30 WEDNESDAY

31 THURSDAY

FRIDAY 1

SATURDAY 2

Ramadan Begins

SUNDAY 3

NOTES

4   **MONDAY**

5   **TUESDAY**

6   **WEDNESDAY**

7   **THURSDAY**

FRIDAY 8

SATURDAY 9

SUNDAY 10

NOTES

POWERED BY PLANKS

F	S	S	M	T	W	T	F	S	S	M	T	W	T	F	S	S	M	T	W	T	F	S	S	M	T	W	T	F	S
1	2	3	4	5	6	7	8	9	10	11	12	13	14	15	16	17	18	19	20	21	22	23	24	25	26	27	28	29	30

11 MONDAY

12 TUESDAY

13 WEDNESDAY

14 THURSDAY

FRIDAY 15

Good Friday / Passover Begins

SATURDAY 16

Easter Sunday

SUNDAY 17

NOTES

F	S	S	M	T	W	T	F	S	S	M	T	W	T	F	S	S	M	T	W	T	F	S	S	M	T	W	T	F	S
1	2	3	4	5	6	7	8	9	10	11	12	13	14	15	16	17	18	19	20	21	22	23	24	25	26	27	28	29	30

18 MONDAY

Easter Monday

19 TUESDAY

20 WEDNESDAY

21 THURSDAY

FRIDAY 22

St. George's Day

SATURDAY 23

A

SUNDAY 24

NOTES

SUBJECT

TO DO

....

....

....

....

....

....

....

....

....

....

....

....

25 MONDAY

26 TUESDAY

27 WEDNESDAY

28 THURSDAY

FRIDAY 29

SATURDAY 30

M

SUNDAY 1

NOTES

2 MONDAY

3 TUESDAY

4 WEDNESDAY

5 THURSDAY

FRIDAY 6

SATURDAY 7

M

SUNDAY 8

NOTES

S M T W T F S S M T W T F S S M T W T F S S M T W T F S S M T
1 2 3 4 5 6 7 8 9 10 11 12 13 14 15 16 17 18 19 20 21 22 23 24 25 26 27 28 29 30 31

9   MONDAY

10 TUESDAY

11 WEDNESDAY

12 THURSDAY

FRIDAY 13

SATURDAY 14

M

SUNDAY 15

NOTES

S	M	T	W	T	F	S	S	M	T	W	T	F	S	S	M	T	W	T	F	S	S	M	T	W	T	F	S	S	M	T
1	2	3	4	5	6	7	8	9	10	11	12	13	14	15	16	17	18	19	20	21	22	23	24	25	26	27	28	29	30	31

16 MONDAY

17 TUESDAY

18 WEDNESDAY

19 THURSDAY

FRIDAY 20

SATURDAY 21

M

SUNDAY 22

NOTES

S	M	T	W	T	F	S	S	M	T	W	T	F	S	S	M	T	W	T	F	S	S	M	T	W	T	F	S	S	M	T
1	2	3	4	5	6	7	8	9	10	11	12	13	14	15	16	17	18	19	20	21	22	23	24	25	26	27	28	29	30	31

23 MONDAY

24 TUESDAY

25 WEDNESDAY

26 THURSDAY

FRIDAY 27

SATURDAY 28

M

SUNDAY 29

NOTES

S	M	T	W	T	F	S	S	M	T	W	T	F	S	S	M	T	W	T	F	S	S	M	T	W	T	F	S	S	M	T
1	2	3	4	5	6	7	8	9	10	11	12	13	14	15	16	17	18	19	20	21	22	23	24	25	26	27	28	29	30	31

JUNE

TO DO ....

30 MONDAY

31 TUESDAY

1 WEDNESDAY

2 THURSDAY

Queen's Platinum Jubilee Bank Holiday

Queen's Platinum Jubilee Bank Holiday

FRIDAY 3

SATURDAY 4

J

SUNDAY 5

NOTES

6 MONDAY

7 TUESDAY

8 WEDNESDAY

9 THURSDAY

FRIDAY 10

SATURDAY 11

SUNDAY 12

NOTES

W	T	F	S	S	M	T	W	T	F	S	S	M	T	W	T	F	S	S	M	T	W	T	F	S	S	M	T	W	T
1	2	3	4	5	6	7	8	9	10	11	12	13	14	15	16	17	18	19	20	21	22	23	24	25	26	27	28	29	30

13 MONDAY

14 TUESDAY

15 WEDNESDAY

16 THURSDAY

FRIDAY 17

SATURDAY 18

Father's Day

SUNDAY 19

NOTES

W	T	F	S	S	M	T	W	T	F	S	S	M	T	W	T	F	S	S	M	T	W	T	F	S	S	M	T	W	T
1	2	3	4	5	6	7	8	9	10	11	12	13	14	15	16	17	18	19	20	21	22	23	24	25	26	27	28	29	30

20 MONDAY

21 TUESDAY

22 WEDNESDAY

23 THURSDAY

FRIDAY 24

SATURDAY 25

SUNDAY 26

NOTES

SUZIE &
DUSTY
6.62607004

W	T	F	S	S	M	T	W	T	F	S	S	M	T	W	T	F	S	S	M	T	W	T	F	S	S	M	T	W	T
1	2	3	4	5	6	7	8	9	10	11	12	13	14	15	16	17	18	19	20	21	22	23	24	25	26	27	28	29	30

JULY

TO DO ....

....

....

....

....

....

....

....

....

....

....

....

....

....

27 MONDAY

28 TUESDAY

29 WEDNESDAY

30 THURSDAY

FRIDAY 1

SATURDAY 2

SUNDAY 3

NOTES

4   MONDAY

5   TUESDAY

6   WEDNESDAY

7   THURSDAY

FRIDAY 8

SATURDAY 9

SUNDAY 10

NOTES

11 MONDAY

12 TUESDAY

Battle of the Boyne (Northern Ireland)

13 WEDNESDAY

14 THURSDAY

FRIDAY 15

SATURDAY 16

J

SUNDAY 17

NOTES

JULY 2022

18 MONDAY

19 TUESDAY

20 WEDNESDAY

21 THURSDAY

FRIDAY 22

SATURDAY 23

SUNDAY 24

J

NOTES

F	S	S	M	T	W	T	F	S	S	M	T	W	T	F	S	S	M	T	W	T	F	S	S	M	T	W	T	F	S	S
1	2	3	4	5	6	7	8	9	10	11	12	13	14	15	16	17	18	19	20	21	22	23	24	25	26	27	28	29	30	31

25 MONDAY

26 TUESDAY

27 WEDNESDAY

28 THURSDAY

FRIDAY 29

Islamic New Year Begins

....
....
....
....
....
....

SATURDAY 30

....
....
....
....
....
....

J

SUNDAY 31

....
....
....
....
....
....

NOTES

....
....
....

F	S	S	M	T	W	T	F	S	S	M	T	W	T	F	S	S	M	T	W	T	F	S	S	M	T	W	T	F	S	S
1	2	3	4	5	6	7	8	9	10	11	12	13	14	15	16	17	18	19	20	21	22	23	24	25	26	27	28	29	30	31

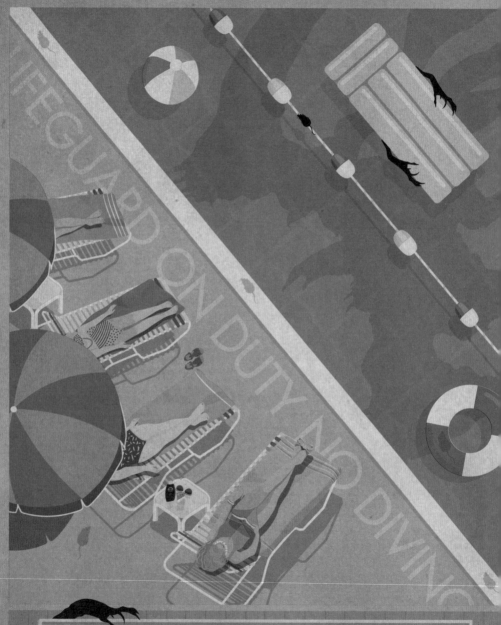

HAWKINS COMMUNITY POOL

AUGUST

TO DO ....

....

....

....

....

....

....

....

....

....

....

....

....

....

1 MONDAY

Summer Bank Holiday (Scotland)

2 TUESDAY

3 WEDNESDAY

4 THURSDAY

FRIDAY 5

SATURDAY 6

SUNDAY 7

A

NOTES

8 MONDAY

9 TUESDAY

10 WEDNESDAY

11 THURSDAY

FRIDAY 12

SATURDAY 13

SUNDAY 14

A

NOTES

M	T	W	T	F	S	S	M	T	W	T	F	S	S	M	T	W	T	F	S	S	M	T	W	T	F	S	S	M	T	W
1	2	3	4	5	6	7	8	9	10	11	12	13	14	15	16	17	18	19	20	21	22	23	24	25	26	27	28	29	30	31

15 MONDAY

16 TUESDAY

17 WEDNESDAY

18 THURSDAY

FRIDAY 19

SATURDAY 20

SUNDAY 21

A

NOTES

M	T	W	T	F	S	S	M	T	W	T	F	S	S	M	T	W	T	F	S	S	M	T	W	T	F	S	S	M	T	W
1	2	3	4	5	6	7	8	9	10	11	12	13	14	15	16	17	18	19	20	21	22	23	24	25	26	27	28	29	30	31

22 MONDAY

23 TUESDAY

24 WEDNESDAY

25 THURSDAY

FRIDAY 26

SATURDAY 27

SUNDAY 28

A

NOTES

M	T	W	T	F	S	S	M	T	W	T	F	S	S	M	T	W	T	F	S	S	M	T	W	T	F	S	S	M	T	W
1	2	3	4	5	6	7	8	9	10	11	12	13	14	15	16	17	18	19	20	21	22	23	24	25	26	27	28	29	30	31

HAWKINS NATIONAL LABORATORY
U.S. DEPT OF ENERGY

S P E C I E S

DEMOGORGON

MAN WITH NO FAC
MAN WITH NO FAC
MAN WITH NO FAC

M O N
S T E

MAN WITH NO FACE   MAN WIT   FACE
MAN WITH NO FACE   MAN WI   O FACE
MAN WITH NO FACE   MAN W   O FACE

SEPTEMBER

TO DO ....

....

....

....

....

....

....

....

....

....

....

....

....

....

29 MONDAY

Summer Bank Holiday (ENG, NIR, WAL)

30 TUESDAY

31 WEDNESDAY

1 THURSDAY

FRIDAY 2

SATURDAY 3

SUNDAY 4

S

NOTES

CHOCOLATE
PUDDING

---

5 **MONDAY**

6 **TUESDAY**

7 **WEDNESDAY**

8 **THURSDAY**

FRIDAY 9

SATURDAY 10

SUNDAY 11

S

NOTES

T	F	S	S	M	T	W	T	F	S	S	M	T	W	T	F	S	S	M	T	W	T	F	S	S	M	T	W	T	F
1	2	3	4	5	6	7	8	9	10	11	12	13	14	15	16	17	18	19	20	21	22	23	24	25	26	27	28	29	30

SEPTEMBER 2022

12 MONDAY

13 TUESDAY

14 WEDNESDAY

15 THURSDAY

FRIDAY 16

SATURDAY 17

SUNDAY 18

S

NOTES

CHOCOLATE
PUDDING

T	F	S	S	M	T	W	T	F	S	S	M	T	W	T	F	S	S	M	T	W	T	F	S	S	M	T	W	T	F
1	2	3	4	5	6	7	8	9	10	11	12	13	14	15	16	17	18	19	20	21	22	23	24	25	26	27	28	29	30

19 MONDAY

20 TUESDAY

21 WEDNESDAY

The United Nations International Day of Peace

22 THURSDAY

FRIDAY 23

SATURDAY 24

Rosh Hashanah (Jewish New Year) Begins

SUNDAY 25

S

NOTES

CHOCOLATE
PUDDING

OCTOBER

TO DO ....

....

....

....

....

....

....

....

....

....

....

....

....

....

....

26 MONDAY

27 TUESDAY

28 WEDNESDAY

29 THURSDAY

FRIDAY 30

....

....

....

....

....

....

SATURDAY 1

....

....

....

....

....

....

SUNDAY 2

....

....

....

....

....

....

NOTES

....

....

....

....

F	S	S	M	T	W	T	F	S	S	M	T	W	T	F	S	S	M	T	W	T	F	S	S	M	T	W	T	F	S
16	17	18	19	20	21	22	23	24	25	26	27	28	29	30	1	2	3	4	5	6	7	8	9	10	11	12	13	14	15

3 MONDAY

4 TUESDAY

Yom Kippur Begins

5 WEDNESDAY

6 THURSDAY

FRIDAY 7

SATURDAY 8

SUNDAY 9

NOTES

S S M T W T F S S M T W T F S S M T W T F S S M T W T F S S M
1 2 3 4 5 6 7 8 9 10 11 12 13 14 15 16 17 18 19 20 21 22 23 24 25 26 27 28 29 30 31

10 MONDAY

11 TUESDAY

12 WEDNESDAY

13 THURSDAY

FRIDAY 14

SATURDAY 15

SUNDAY 16

NOTES

17 MONDAY

18 TUESDAY

19 WEDNESDAY

20 THURSDAY

FRIDAY 21

SATURDAY 22

SUNDAY 23

NOTES

24 MONDAY

Diwa

25 TUESDAY

26 WEDNESDAY

27 THURSDAY

FRIDAY 28

SATURDAY 29

Daylight Saving Time Ends

SUNDAY 30

NOTES

DART

S	S	M	T	W	T	F	S	S	M	T	W	T	F	S	S	M	T	W	T	F	S	S	M	T	W	T	F	S	S	M
1	2	3	4	5	6	7	8	9	10	11	12	13	14	15	16	17	18	19	20	21	22	23	24	25	26	27	28	29	30	31

NOVEMBER

TO DO ....

....

....

....

....

....

....

....

....

....

....

....

....

....

31 MONDAY

1 TUESDAY

2 WEDNESDAY

3 THURSDAY

FRIDAY 4

Guy Fawkes Night

SATURDAY 5

SUNDAY 6

NOTES

S	M	T	W	T	F	S	S	M	T	W	T	F	S	S	M	T	W	T	F	S	S	M	T	W	T	F	S	S	M	T
16	17	18	19	20	21	22	23	24	25	26	27	28	29	30	31	1	2	3	4	5	6	7	8	9	10	11	12	13	14	15

NOVEMBER 2022

7   MONDAY

8   TUESDAY

9   WEDNESDAY

10 THURSDAY

FRIDAY 11

SATURDAY 12

Remembrance Sunday

SUNDAY 13

NOTES

DUSTIN

N

14 MONDAY

15 TUESDAY

16 WEDNESDAY

17 THURSDAY

FRIDAY 18

SATURDAY 19

SUNDAY 20

NOTES

T	W	T	F	S	S	M	T	W	T	F	S	S	M	T	W	T	F	S	S	M	T	W	T	F	S	S	M	T	W
1	2	3	4	5	6	7	8	9	10	11	12	13	14	15	16	17	18	19	20	21	22	23	24	25	26	27	28	29	30

21 MONDAY

22 TUESDAY

23 WEDNESDAY

24 THURSDAY

FRIDAY 25

SATURDAY 26

SUNDAY 27

NOTES

Scoops
Troop

3

Erica **Dustin** Robyn **Steve** Erica **Dustin** Robyn **Steve** Erica **Dusti**

DECEMBER

TO DO ....

....

....

....

....

....

....

....

....

....

....

....

....

....

....

....

28 MONDAY

29 TUESDAY

30 WEDNESDAY

St. Andrew's Day (Scotland)

1 THURSDAY

FRIDAY 2

SATURDAY 3

SUNDAY 4

NOTES

KEEP YOUR CURIOSITY DOOR OPEN

D

W	T	F	S	S	M	T	W	T	F	S	S	M	T	W	T	F	S	S	M	T	W	T	F	S	S	M	T	W	T
16	17	18	19	20	21	22	23	24	25	26	27	28	29	30	1	2	3	4	5	6	7	8	9	10	11	12	13	14	15

5 MONDAY

6 TUESDAY

7 WEDNESDAY

8 THURSDAY

FRIDAY 9

SATURDAY 10

SUNDAY 11

NOTES

T	F	S	S	M	T	W	T	F	S	S	M	T	W	T	F	S	S	M	T	W	T	F	S	S	M	T	W	T	F	S
1	2	3	4	5	6	7	8	9	10	11	12	13	14	15	16	17	18	19	20	21	22	23	24	25	26	27	28	29	30	31

12 MONDAY

13 TUESDAY

14 WEDNESDAY

15 THURSDAY

FRIDAY 16

SATURDAY 17

SUNDAY 18

NOTES

19 MONDAY

20 TUESDAY

21 WEDNESDAY

22 THURSDAY

FRIDAY 23

SATURDAY 24

Christmas Day

SUNDAY 25

NOTES

KEEP YOUR
CURIOUSITY
DOOR OPEN

T	F	S	S	M	T	W	T	F	S	S	M	T	W	T	F	S	S	M	T	W	T	F	S	S	M	T	W	T	F	S
1	2	3	4	5	6	7	8	9	10	11	12	13	14	15	16	17	18	19	20	21	22	23	24	25	26	27	28	29	30	31

DECEMBER 2022

26 MONDAY

Boxing Day

27 TUESDAY

Bank Holiday

28 WEDNESDAY

29 THURSDAY

FRIDAY 30

New Year's Eve

SATURDAY 31

New Year's Day

SUNDAY 1

NOTES

KEEP YOUR CURIOUSITY DOOR OPEN

J

PLANNER 2023

JANUARY	FEBRUARY	MARCH
1 S	1 W	1 W
2 M	2 T	2 T
3 T	3 F	3 F
4 W	4 S	4 S
5 T	5 S	5 S
6 F	6 M	6 M
7 S	7 T	7 T
8 S	8 W	8 W
9 M	9 T	9 T
10 T	10 F	10 F
11 W	11 S	11 S
12 T	12 S	12 S
13 F	13 M	13 M
14 S	14 T	14 T
15 S	15 W	15 W
16 M	16 T	16 T
17 T	17 F	17 F
18 W	18 S	18 S
19 T	19 S	19 S
20 F	20 M	20 M
21 S	21 T	21 T
22 S	22 W	22 W
23 M	23 T	23 T
24 T	24 F	24 F
25 W	25 S	25 S
26 T	26 S	26 S
27 F	27 M	27 M
28 S	28 T	28 T
29 S		29 W
30 M		30 T
31 T		31 F

APRIL	MAY	JUNE
1 S	1 M	1 T
2 S	2 T	2 F
3 M	3 W	3 S
4 T	4 T	4 S
5 W	5 F	5 M
6 T	6 S	6 T
7 F	7 S	7 W
8 S	8 M	8 T
9 S	9 T	9 F
10 M	10 W	10 S
11 T	11 T	11 S
12 W	12 F	12 M
13 T	13 S	13 T
14 F	14 S	14 W
15 S	15 M	15 T
16 S	16 T	16 F
17 M	17 W	17 S
18 T	18 T	18 S
19 W	19 F	19 M
20 T	20 S	20 T
21 F	21 S	21 W
22 S	22 M	22 T
23 S	23 T	23 F
24 M	24 W	24 S
25 T	25 T	25 S
26 W	26 F	26 M
27 T	27 S	27 T
28 F	28 S	28 W
29 S	29 M	29 T
30 S	30 T	30 F
	31 W	

PLANNER 2023

JULY	AUGUST	SEPTEMBER
1 S	1 T	1 F
2 S	2 W	2 S
3 M	3 T	3 S
4 T	4 F	4 M
5 W	5 S	5 T
6 T	6 S	6 W
7 F	7 M	7 T
8 S	8 T	8 F
9 S	9 W	9 S
10 M	10 T	10 S
11 T	11 F	11 M
12 W	12 S	12 T
13 T	13 S	13 W
14 F	14 M	14 T
15 S	15 T	15 F
16 S	16 W	16 S
17 M	17 T	17 S
18 T	18 F	18 M
19 W	19 S	19 T
20 T	20 S	20 W
21 F	21 M	21 T
22 S	22 T	22 F
23 S	23 W	23 S
24 M	24 T	24 S
25 T	25 F	25 M
26 W	26 S	26 T
27 T	27 S	27 W
28 F	28 M	28 T
29 S	29 T	29 F
30 S	30 W	30 S
31 M	31 T	

OCTOBER	NOVEMBER	DECEMBER
1 S	1 W	1 F
2 M	2 T	2 S
3 T	3 F	3 S
4 W	4 S	4 M
5 T	5 S	5 T
6 F	6 M	6 W
7 S	7 T	7 T
8 S	8 W	8 F
9 M	9 T	9 S
10 T	10 F	10 S
11 W	11 S	11 M
12 T	12 S	12 T
13 F	13 M	13 W
14 S	14 T	14 T
15 S	15 W	15 F
16 M	16 T	16 S
17 T	17 F	17 S
18 W	18 S	18 M
19 T	19 S	19 T
20 F	20 M	20 W
21 S	21 T	21 T
22 S	22 W	22 F
23 M	23 T	23 S
24 T	24 F	24 S
25 W	25 S	25 M
26 T	26 S	26 T
27 F	27 M	27 W
28 S	28 T	28 T
29 S	29 W	29 F
30 M	30 T	30 S
31 T		31 S

ADDRESS / PHONE NUMBERS

NAME

ADDRESS

TELEPHONE   **MOBILE**

EMAIL

NAME

ADDRESS

TELEPHONE   **MOBILE**

EMAIL

NAME

ADDRESS

TELEPHONE   **MOBILE**

EMAIL

NAME

ADDRESS

TELEPHONE   **MOBILE**

EMAIL

NAME

ADDRESS

TELEPHONE   **MOBILE**

EMAIL

NAME

ADDRESS

TELEPHONE   **MOBILE**

EMAIL

NAME

ADDRESS

TELEPHONE   MOBILE

EMAIL

NAME

ADDRESS

TELEPHONE   MOBILE

EMAIL

NAME

ADDRESS

TELEPHONE   MOBILE

EMAIL

NAME

ADDRESS

TELEPHONE   MOBILE

EMAIL

NAME

ADDRESS

TELEPHONE   MOBILE

EMAIL

NAME

ADDRESS

TELEPHONE   MOBILE

EMAIL

NOTES

NOTES